Usborne English R

Level 3

Frankenstein

Retold by Mairi Mackinnon

Illustrated by Daniele Dickmann

English language consultant: Peter Viney

Contents

You can listen to the story online here:
www.usborneenglishreaders.com/
frankenstein

"Captain Walton, there's someone out there!"

"Impossible!" Their ship was far from land, with the Arctic ice all around. The captain looked where the man was pointing, and saw a dark shape. It was a dog sled, and on it there was another man – a giant, he seemed. The sled raced past them and disappeared. Were they imagining things?

A few hours later, the ice began to break up, but it was still dangerous, and Captain Walton didn't want to sail further before the next day.

In the morning, the captain heard shouts. He joined the men on the ship's deck, and saw another dog sled. It was floating on a piece of ice. There was a man on it, but he looked close to death, and only one of his dogs was still alive.

"Let us help you!" the sailors shouted. "Where are you going?"

"North!" the man answered weakly, and the sailors carried him onto the ship. He was almost frozen, and completely exhausted, but his eyes were still bright.

For two weeks he rested, eating a little and growing stronger each day. At first, Captain Walton didn't want to worry him with questions, but finally the stranger said:

"I want to tell you my story. You may find it hard to believe, but please listen. I have made some terrible mistakes. I don't want anyone else to do the same."

My name is Victor Frankenstein. I come from a good family in Geneva. My father married rather late in life, and my parents were able to travel around Europe until I was born. They loved each other and they loved me very much. They wanted more children, but for some years I was an only child.

When I was six years old, my mother visited a poor family in Italy. They had five children. The youngest was a little girl with fair hair. The family explained that her parents had died, and she was an orphan. They had cared for her until now, but they didn't know how they could continue. My mother offered to adopt the little girl. She had been so kind to the family that they agreed.

And so I had a dear friend and companion, Elizabeth. Two years later, my brother Ernest was born, and five years after that, another brother, little William.

We went to live in the country outside Geneva, and I had the happiest childhood. I didn't have many friends at school except for one boy, Henry Clerval, but I had my loving parents, my sweet Elizabeth and my two brothers.

I was a child who loved reading and studying. I was fascinated by science, and especially the science of living things. When I was old enough, I went to study at the university of Ingolstadt in Germany.

The first terrible thing happened before I left. My mother became ill with a fever, and she never recovered. Elizabeth and I were with her before she died. "My dear children," she said, "take good care of your father and your brothers. I have always hoped that you two will get married one day. Promise me that, and I shall die happy."

There was no medicine and no science that could save her. I felt so helpless!

When I arrived at the university, I studied night and day. My teachers were amazed. Soon I knew almost as much as they did, but I wanted more. I wanted to discover the secret of life itself. I experimented with electricity, and with the bodies of dead people. I saw how the bodies decayed after death. I wondered whether I could stop that decay, and even reverse it?

I began to make a body, using parts of other bodies. To make my work easier, I used the largest parts I could find. The thing that I made was a giant, taller than any man.

I was too busy to eat or sleep, and I stayed in my rooms for days. Letters arrived from my family, but I didn't read them. Then, one autumn night, I forced electricity through the thing that I was making, and it opened its eyes. I looked down at its horrible greenish-white face and its black mouth. What had I done?

I was exhausted. I fell into bed and slept, but my dreams were horrible. When I woke, the monster was standing beside my bed and looking down at me.

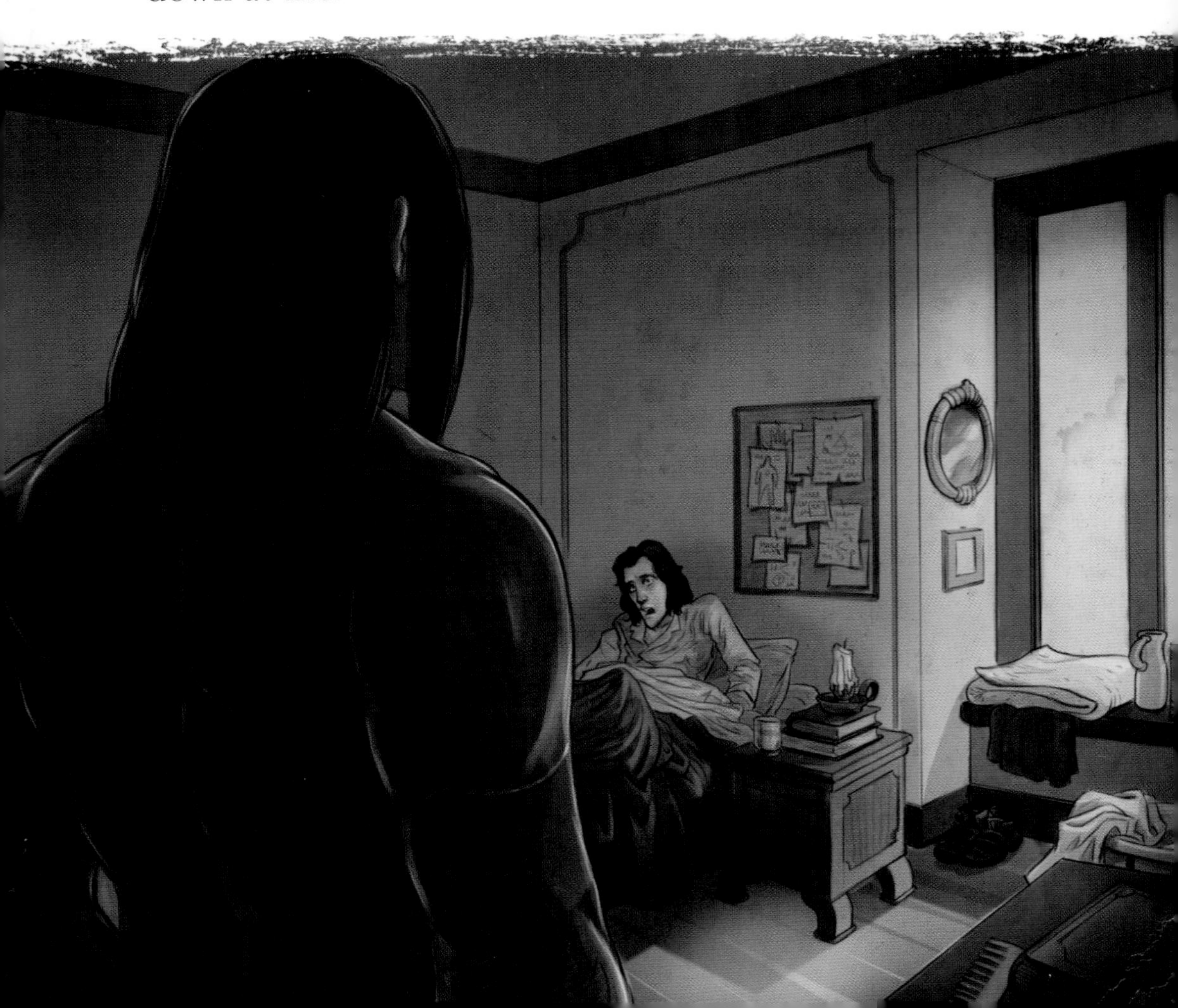

I was terrified. I ran out of the room and through the town, until I came to the inn where coaches arrived from other cities. I recognized the coach from Geneva. Someone was just stepping out of it – someone that I knew well.

"Henry, my friend!"

"Victor! We were so worried. What has happened to you?"

I was shaking with fever. "Where are your rooms? Let me come with you."

I didn't dare to think what we might find there, but the rooms were empty. The monster had gone.

All winter Clerval cared for me, and by the spring I was much better. Then a letter arrived from my father.

Geneva May 5th

My dear Victor,

I was so glad to hear that you are recovering. I am sorry to write to you with this shocking news.

William is dead, that dear, sweet boy. We were walking one evening outside the town. It was almost dark when Ernest noticed that William wasn't with us. We searched all night, and in the morning we found his body. There were marks around his neck. Someone had strangled him.

Elizabeth blames herself. William wanted to borrow a little picture of your mother, in a gold frame, and she gave it to him. When we found him, the picture was missing. I suppose the murderer wanted the gold – but who would kill a little child?

I arranged to go home immediately. When the coach was near Geneva, I decided to stop and visit the place where William was last seen. There was a terrible storm, with flashes of lightning across the lake. Suddenly I saw a giant shape between the trees. Surely it couldn't be... but yes, it was the monster! I guessed immediately that he was William's murderer. He raced away towards the top of the mountain. No human could ever run fast enough to catch him.

All night, I walked by the lake in the storm. Who would believe my story? Finally I reached my father's house. My brother Ernest met me.

"Oh, Victor, I'm glad that you're here. Nobody can calm Elizabeth. William's death was bad enough – but the murderer was someone we knew!"

"What do you mean?"

"It was our servant Justine. Elizabeth was so kind to her, and we trusted her completely. We thought that she loved little William."

"It can't be!"

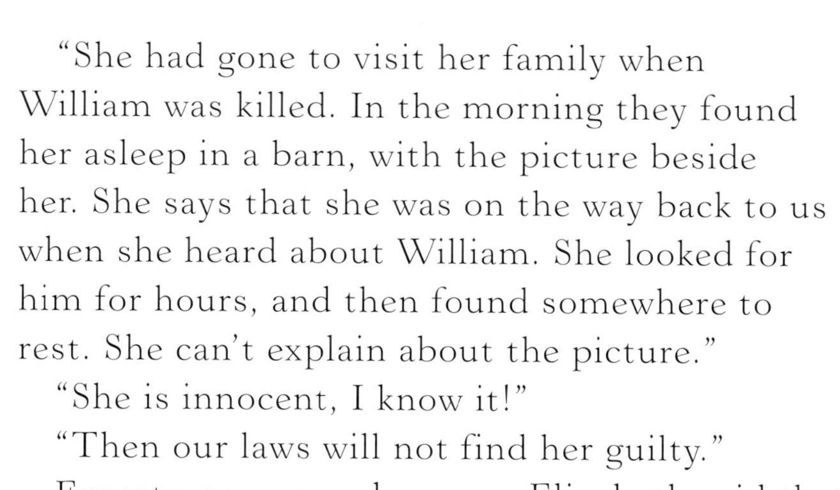

"She had gone to visit her family when William was killed. In the morning they found her asleep in a barn, with the picture beside her. She says that she was on the way back to us when she heard about William. She looked for him for hours, and then found somewhere to rest. She can't explain about the picture."

"She is innocent, I know it!"

"Then our laws will not find her guilty."

Ernest was wrong, however. Elizabeth said that she believed Justine, but she could not persuade the townspeople. Justine was condemned to death, and hanged two weeks later.

If I was right, the monster was responsible – which meant *I* was responsible – for the deaths of two innocent people. Could anyone ever forgive me? I avoided everyone, walking far into the mountains, higher and higher until I reached the mountain tops. There, in the fresh snow, I saw the giant coming towards me.

"You evil monster!" I shouted. I ran towards him, but he avoided me easily.

"Wait," he said. "I understand why you hate me, but you made me and so you must listen to me. If I have done terrible things, it is because I am miserable. You can make me good by giving me happiness."

I listened, horrified but fascinated, as the monster told his story.

"I don't remember much about the time after you made me," he said. "I learned to open and close my eyes, to move my arms and legs. My body was cold, and I found some of your clothes to cover it. I was hungry and thirsty, but there was no food or drink. I walked all night until I was far from the town. I found some fruit trees near a river, and I ate and drank and slept.

Then the rain and snow came, so I looked for a place where I could be warm and dry. I saw a hut near the river, and went towards it. There was a man there, and he had made a fire. When he saw me, he screamed and ran away. I didn't understand why, but his fire was warm and bright, and he had even left a little food.

When the food was finished and the fire died, I went out again. I walked until I came to a village. As soon as the villagers saw me, they shouted and threw stones. The men started running towards me. I understood that they wanted to hurt me, and I ran. Why were people afraid of me? I wanted to understand them better, but I could not show myself.

At last I found another empty hut, next to a small house. I could watch the people in the house through a hole in the wall, but they couldn't see me.

I was fascinated by them. There was an old man, a young man named Felix and a young woman, Agatha. Felix and Agatha took care of the old man, and I realized that he was blind.

They lived very simply. Often the young people gave their father food but ate nothing themselves. At first, I didn't understand them when they spoke, but slowly I learned their words. Sometimes Agatha helped the village children to learn their letters, and so, by watching and listening, I learned to read too.

In the evenings, Felix and Agatha read books to the old man, and I learned many things about the world from what I heard.

I helped them in little ways. I could see that they needed wood for their fire, so when they were sleeping, I collected some and left it outside their door. I left presents of wild fruit, too. They were surprised and pleased, but they never guessed that their helper was so close.

I lived like this for many months. I wanted to speak to them, but I knew I couldn't. I had seen my face in a pool of water, and I understood now why people screamed when they saw me. I was an ugly monster – but I wanted to be like these people, kind and good!

Still, if the old man was blind, he would not see my face. I could speak to him first, and he could explain me to his children. I chose a day when the young people were out of the house, and went inside. The old man spoke to me politely and listened kindly; but then we heard the young people coming back.

When she saw me, Agatha screamed and Felix attacked me. "Get away from my father!" he shouted. I didn't fight him. I just ran into the forest.

When I came back to the house, it was empty. Now I was angry. The family had been cruel, and I could not forgive them. I put dry wood all around the house, took a piece from the fire inside and lit it. I watched while the house and my hut burned to the ground.

Where could I go now? There were some letters in your old clothes, with your father's name and address. I didn't know where Geneva was, and it was months before I came close to the town. I avoided people as much as I could, but one evening I saw a little boy playing on his own. I thought that maybe he would not hate me, and I went towards him.

When he saw me, he screamed, "Go away! I'm not afraid of you. My father is an important man. His name is Frankenstein!"

It was your name, the name of my enemy! I held his neck until he was quiet. I had killed him. He had a picture in his pocket of a beautiful lady. I was looking at it when I heard other people coming, and I ran away.

I looked for somewhere to hide, and found a barn. I thought that it was empty, but then I saw a young woman asleep. I wanted to wake her, to hear her speak kindly, but I knew that she would scream, too. Instead I left the picture beside her, and hid in some trees.

In the morning, I heard shouting. A crowd was dragging the young woman out of the barn. Their faces were full of hate, and she was crying.

Some days later, I went back to the place where I had killed the boy. There was someone else there. It was you! You, who brought me into this life of hate and pain. I was too angry to speak to you, but since then I have been thinking. You can make the one thing that will end my unhappiness. You must make another one like me – a companion – a wife."

I stared at him. "You killed my brother," I said at last. "Because of you, an innocent girl was condemned to death; and you ask me to make you happy? To bring another monster into the world, to murder and destroy? I won't do it!"

The monster looked furiously angry, and then he controlled himself. "You are wrong," he said. "I have done all these things because I am unhappy and alone. Make a companion for me, and I promise that we will hide. We will be far away, in the wild places where humans never go, and you will have peace. If you refuse, I will hurt your family again. I cannot force you to love me, but I can make you fear me." He turned around and left me on the mountain.

Slowly, I climbed down. Did I dare to make a companion, and trust the monster to keep his promise? Or should I refuse, and risk his anger? What might he do to me or, even worse, to my family? I decided that I had to trust him.

I couldn't possibly do this horrible work at home. I told my father that I wanted to travel to Britain and meet some of the great scientists there. Clerval could travel with me. I planned to return in less than a year, and then Elizabeth and I could get married and be happy at last.

Clerval and I went to visit some friends in Scotland. I needed to find somewhere quiet and private, so I told Clerval that I wanted to travel on my own to the northern islands. It was easy to find a house there where I could work in peace. I brought in everything I needed, and started my experiments.

This time, my work was very different. I knew what I was doing – but also, I knew what I had done. How could I be sure of my results? This new monster might be even worse than the first one, and *she* had made no promise to me.

One evening, I looked at the thing. It was almost finished, and it was disgusting. Then I heard a sound, and looked towards the window. The monster was there, watching me! I screamed, and began to destroy the thing that I had made.

I heard another, louder scream outside the window. "How dare you take happiness away from me? Oh, I will make your life miserable. I will find you, wherever you are. *I will be with you on your wedding night*." I ran out of the house, but he was gone.

The next morning, a letter arrived from Clerval. He was coming to meet me before we returned to Switzerland. I was glad to hear this, but first I had something to do. That evening, I packed the broken pieces of my experiment into a small boat, and sailed away from the island. When I was far out on the sea, I threw everything into the water. Then I meant to rest a little, but I was so tired that I fell asleep.

When I woke, I could see land, but it wasn't my island. There was a small village ahead, and I sailed towards it. I saw people pointing at my boat, but they didn't look friendly. As soon as I arrived, they took hold of me and dragged me away to prison.

"What kind of a welcome is this?" I asked.

"Murderer! What kind of a welcome do you expect?"

Who was this murderer? I felt sick with fear. The villagers told me that they had seen a strange man in a boat. Soon after, they found the dead man's body. The next day, they took me to see it. Just as I had guessed, it was Clerval. I could see the huge fingermarks around his neck.

I was ill for several months. The villagers soon decided that I was not guilty – people had seen me on my island, far away, around the time of Clerval's death – but I knew that I was responsible. My father came to bring me home, and we left as soon as I was well enough to travel. I wanted to be with my family. I knew that the monster would come back.

"I will be with you on your wedding night." If he planned to destroy me, then at least my miserable life would be over; but maybe he wouldn't succeed. Maybe I would have the strength to kill him at last.

Elizabeth was worried because I was so thin and pale. I saw that she, too, was paler and sadder, but still beautiful. We decided to have a quiet wedding at home, and afterwards we planned to travel to Italy, the land of her childhood. In the days before the wedding I was always nervous, and I carried guns with me everywhere, but I never saw the monster.

After the wedding, we crossed Lake Geneva by boat. We arrived on the south side in the early evening, and walked a little beside the lake.

When night came, I was more nervous than ever. I told Elizabeth to go into the inn where we were staying. I wanted to look all around it, to see if the monster was hiding nearby. I didn't find him in the garden or the trees, but then I heard a terrible scream.

Elizabeth was lying across the bed, like a broken toy. I could see the heavy fingermarks around her neck.

The window was open, and for a moment I saw the monster's evil face before he climbed down the wall outside. I fired both my guns, but I missed and he ran towards the lake and jumped into the water.

What a fool I had been! I had expected him to attack me, when all along he planned to hurt Elizabeth. It was too horrible to think about.

I went back to Geneva, to my brother and my poor father. The news was too much for my father, after all that he had suffered. A few days later he, too, was dead.

For some months, I was between life and death, between sickness and madness. Slowly I recovered. Now only one thing mattered to me. I must find the monster and destroy him. I must follow him, even if he went to the ends of the earth. I went further and further north. I never saw him, but he left me messages and signs, and sometimes even food. I understood that he wanted to keep me alive – alive and miserable. Finally, here on the Arctic ice, I saw him, but I wasn't strong enough to follow. He is out there still, and I must find him.

Frankenstein lay back, exhausted. Captain Walton asked the ship's doctor to give him some medicine, but it was already too late. An hour later, Frankenstein closed his eyes for the last time.

Slowly and sadly, the captain left his cabin. What a terrible story! He had liked the man, though, had liked his seriousness and intelligence.

Then he heard a sound behind him, and turned around. The monster almost filled the cabin, leaning over Frankenstein's dead body. Was it possible – was he actually crying?

"If you wanted to kill him yourself, you are too late," said the captain coldly.

"No! I was going to ask him – to forgive me. At first, I only wanted to make him suffer, but it didn't bring me understanding, or happiness. Nothing will do that now.

I am ready to die. I will go on until I can travel no further, and then for the last time I will build a fire and let it destroy me. You are the last human that I will ever see. Soon I will be gone forever. Goodbye."

He climbed out of the cabin window, and jumped down onto the floating ice. The waves carried him away from the ship, into the darkness and distance.

About the story

In the summer of 1816, Mary Godwin was just eighteen years old when she visited Switzerland with her friends, the poets Percy Shelley (later her husband) and Lord Byron. The weather was terrible and they spent days sitting by the fire and reading ghost stories. One day, Byron suggested a competition: they should each write their own horror story.

At first, Mary couldn't think of a story, but then she had the idea of a young student who wanted to discover the secret of life. She imagined her student trying to give life to a dead body... and so began the story of Frankenstein and his monster.

The original story became a book in 1818, with an introduction by Percy Shelley but without Mary Shelley's name. At the time, some readers thought it was brilliant, while others thought it was disgusting and worrying. Two hundred years later, it is one of the best-known and most popular horror stories in history, and has inspired hundreds of books, plays and films.

Activities

The answers are on page 48.

Young Victor Frankenstein

Can you put these pictures and sentences in the right order?

A.

I was a child who loved reading and studying.

B.

My mother offered to adopt the girl.

C.

When I arrived at the university, I studied night and day.

D.

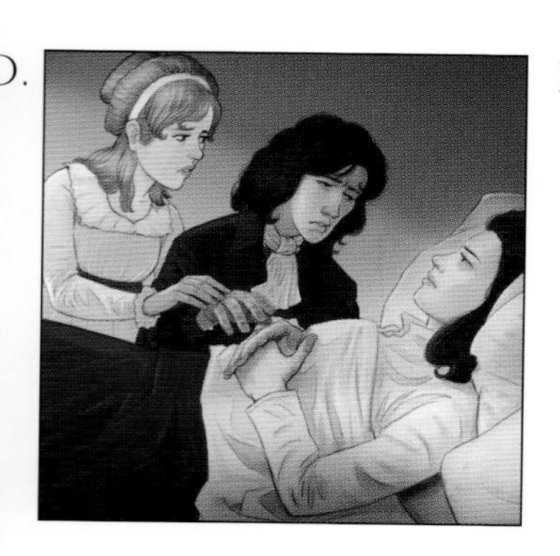

My mother became very ill with a fever.

E.

For some years I was an only child.

F.

I was shaking with fever.

Who's who?

Find *two* sentences that describe each character.

Victor Frankenstein...

Elizabeth...

The monster...

A. ...was Victor's friend at school.

B. ...liked Frankenstein's seriousness and intelligence.

C. ...fell asleep in a barn.

D. ...learned how to read and speak.

E. ...wanted to discover the secret of life.

F. ...was strangled in Scotland.

Henry Clerval... Justine... Captain Walton...

G. ...was adopted by Victor's mother.

H. ...asked the ship's doctor to give Frankenstein some medicine.

I. ...was condemned to death.

J. ...made some terrible mistakes in his life.

K. ...was killed in an inn near Lake Geneva.

L. ...was carried away on the ice.

What the monster learns

Choose one word from the list to finish each sentence.

1. "I learned to .... my arms and legs".

2. 

"I wanted to .... people better."

3. 

"I could .... the people in the house."

4. 

"By watching and listening, I learned to ...."

5. 

" I didn't .... him."

6. 

"I could not .... them."

argue

compare

fight

forgive

invent

move

persuade

read

solve

threaten

understand

watch

What do they want?

Choose the right sentence for each picture.

1.

A. "I wanted to make a dangerous monster."

B. "I wanted to discover the secret of life."

2.

A. "I wanted to hear her speak kindly."

B. "I wanted to make her scream."

3.

A. "I wanted to die in peace."

B. "I wanted to find the monster."

4.

A. "I want to cross the ice and reach land."

B. "I want to build a fire and let it destroy me."

Word list

adopt (v) to agree to act as the parents of a child (who is not your own).

barn (n) a building on a farm, used to store food for animals and farm machines.

cabin (n) a room inside a ship.

childhood (n) the time in your life when you are a child.

coach (n) something that you ride in. In the past, coaches were pulled by horses.

companion (n) a person who spends time with you and shares experiences with you.

condemned to death when you are condemned to death, a law court decides that you must die as punishment for a crime.

decay (v) to become bad or rotten over a period of time.

deck (n) the floor of a boat or ship, especially the outside part above the cabins.

drag (v) to pull someone or something across the ground, with difficulty.

electricity (n) a force which provides light, heat or movement, and which makes machines work.

experiment (v) a scientific exercise where you try something to see whether an idea is true or a process will work.

fascinated (adj) extremely interested.

fever (n) when you have a fever, your body is hot and you feel weak and ill.

fire (v) to shoot a gun.

force (v) to push something violently into or through something else, or to make someone do something.

forgive (v) if you forgive someone, you stop being angry that they have done something wrong.

frame (n) the wood or metal around a picture.

furious (adj) extremely angry.

guilty (adj) if a law court finds you guilty, it decides that you have committed a crime.

hang, hanged (v) in the past, this was a way for the law to kill a guilty person, by tying a rope around their neck and letting their body hang down.

helpless (adj) if you are helpless, you cannot do what you want.

horrified (adj) extremely shocked.

hut (n) a small, simple building (usually too small and simple for people to live in it all the time).

inn (n) a type of hotel where you can pay to eat and sleep when you are on a journey.

innocent (adj) the opposite of guilty. If you are innocent, you have not committed a crime or done anything bad.

lightning (n) when there is a storm, lightning is the sudden very bright light in the sky.

madness (n) being insane and not in your right mind.

murderer (n) a criminal who has killed another person.

nod (v) when you nod, you move your head forward quickly to show that you agree.

orphan (n) a child whose parents are dead.

responsible (adj) if you are responsible for something, either you take care of it (a good thing) or it is your fault (a bad thing).

reverse (v) to turn something around and make it go in the opposite direction.

seriousness (n) having a serious character.

sickness (n) being sick or ill.

sled (n) something that is used to carry heavy things across the snow or ice. Sleds are sometimes pulled by dogs.

strangle (v) to kill someone by putting your hands tightly around their throat so that they cannot breathe.

suffer (v) when you suffer, you feel great pain or sadness.

Answers

Young Victor Frankenstein

E, B, A, D, C, F

What the monster learns

1. move
2. understand
3. watch
4. read
5. fight
6. forgive

Who's who?

Victor Frankenstein – E, J
Elizabeth – G, K
The monster – D, L
Henry Clerval – A, F
Justine – C, I
Captain Walton – B, H

What do they want?

1. B
2. A
3. B
4. B

You can find information about other Usborne English Readers here: www.usborneenglishreaders.com

Designed by Hope Reynolds
Series designer: Laura Nelson
Edited by Jane Chisholm
With thanks to Andy Prentice
Digital imaging: Nick Wakeford

Page 40: picture of Mary Shelley © Granger, NYC/TopFoto

First published in 2018 by Usborne Publishing Ltd.,
Usborne House, 83-85 Saffron Hill, London EC1N 8RT, England.